Computer Kate

Written by Julia Jarman
Illustrated by Robert Geary

Kate was computer crazy.
Kate was computer mad.

Zap! Zap! Zap!
All day long.
It made her poor mum sad.

'Zapping is horrid,' said Mum.
'It isn't,' Computer Kate said.
She went on zapping all day long.
'Zap zap,' she said, 'You're dead.'

Then one day Kate got a new game.
It was called The Monster Bee.

If you want to go to
Monster Land
press the enter key

Kate was computer crazy.
Kate was computer mad.
And so Kate pressed the ENTER key . . .

and wished she never had.

Kate entered her computer.
She went right through the screen.

Then Kate entered
Monster Land . . .

and saw the Monster Queen.

‘Zap! Zap! Zap!’ said the Monster Queen Bee.
‘I zap little girls for tea.’

‘I want to go home,’ said Computer Kate.
‘No no!’ said the Monster Bee.

Queen Bee was computer crazy.
Queen Bee was computer mad.

Zap! Zap! Zap!
All day long.
She made poor Kate feel sad.

'Zapping is horrid,' said Kate.
'It isn't,' said the Monster Bee.

‘So now I’m going to zap you.
And eat you for my tea.’

Kate wanted to go home now.
She wanted to get out.
She saw her mum
through the screen.
She gave her mum a shout.

She shouted, 'Help me! Help me, please!
Look, Mum! Look, it's me!'

Kate's mum looked.
She saw her and . . .

she pressed the EXIT key.